Funster 300+ Riddles
for Bright Kids
and Smart Adults
Easy to Difficult

Charles Timmerman
Founder of Funster.com

A Funster Series Book.
Funster™ and Funster.com™ are trademarks of
Charles Timmerman.

ISBN: 978-1-953561-15-2

Copyediting by Bob Cooper.

A Special Request

Your brief Amazon review could <u>really</u> help us. This link will take you to the Amazon.com review page for this book:

funster.com/review35

Contents

Introduction — 4

Questions — 5

Answers — 76

Introduction

Welcome to this carefully curated collection of curious riddles! They start out fairly simple and progress until they are quite challenging by the end of the book. You'll find a mix of wordplay, logic puzzles, and mathematical conundrums. So, there is something here for everyone at all levels.

Remember, riddles aren't just about finding the answer—they're about the journey you take to get there. These riddles are a way to stretch your mind and see things from a different perspective. As you make your way through these pages, you might be surprised to find that you can solve riddles that once seemed impossible.

Here are a few tips to make this book even more enjoyable:

- It is often a good idea to use paper and pencil. This is especially true with some of the advanced riddles. They would be hard to solve only in your head.

- Share these riddles by challenging your friends and family. It's fun for all and enlightening to see how others unravel these enigmas.

QUESTIONS

1 This fruit gets its name from its color.

2 The more it dries, the wetter it becomes. What is it?

3 I only point in one direction, but I guide people around the world. What am I?

4 One day an alchemist brought a king a bottle holding a strange liquid. The alchemist said, "This liquid I discovered will dissolve anything it touches." How did the king know that he was lying?

5 I am a king but also a common measurement device. What am I?

6   I am the only organ in the human body that named itself. What am I?

7   I go up when the rain comes down. What am I?

8   What has to be broken before it can be used?

9   What can you catch but never throw?

10   I fly all day long but don't go anywhere. What am I?

11   What is black when you buy it, red-hot when you use it, and then cold and gray when you throw it away?

12   This is possibly the world's oldest riddle. It is a Sumerian riddle written on a tablet in the 18th century BC: There is a house. One enters it blind and comes out seeing. What is it?

13   Why is it that whenever you are looking for something, you always find it in the last place you look?

14   If there are 3 apples and you take away 2, how many apples do you have?

15   What invention lets you look right through a wall?

16   My rings are not worth much, but they do tell my age. What am I?

17   What has a head and a tail but no body?

18   I have 3 eye colors: yellow, red, and green. When the red eye appears, everybody freezes. What am I?

19   Trains travel from one town to another town all day, always on the same track, always

going nonstop and at the same speed. The noon train took 80 minutes to complete the trip, but the 4 p.m. train took an hour and 20 minutes. Why?

20 I can go through glass without breaking it. What am I?

21 How many months have 28 days?

22 What kind of coat can be put on only when wet?

23 What building has the most stories?

24 In a one-story gray house, everything is gray. The kitchen is gray, the bedrooms are gray, the bathroom is gray. What color are the stairs?

25 It stalks the countryside with ears that can't hear. What is it?

26   I move without wings between silken strings, I leave as you find my substance behind. What am I?

27   What letter can you drink?

28   Which is heavier: a ton of bricks or a ton of feathers?

29   What can be broken but is right 2 times a day?

30   How much dirt is in a hole 4 feet deep and 2 feet wide?

31   What do you call a man whose children have children of their own?

32   If you were standing directly on Antarctica's South Pole facing north, which direction would you travel if you took one step backward?

33   Boats with holes and dirty
      dishes have this in common.

34   No matter how much rain
      comes down on it, it won't get
      any wetter. What is it?

35   I have many needles, but I do
      not sew. What am I?

36   I am light as a feather, yet the
      strongest man can't hold me
      for more than a few minutes.
      What am I?

37   You are my brother, but I am
      not your brother. Who am I?

38   My tail is long; my coat is
      brown. I like the country; I like
      the town. I can live in a house
      or live in a shed, and I come
      out to play when you are in
      bed. What am I?

39 Each morning, I appear to lie at your feet. All day, I will follow no matter how fast you run, yet I nearly perish in the midday sun. What am I?

40 This famous riddle began as a nursery rhyme in the 17th century. Later, it appeared in the movie *Die Hard with a Vengeance,* where it was solved in 30 seconds to keep a bomb from exploding!
As I was going to St. Ives,
I met a man with seven wives,
Each wife had seven sacks,
Each sack had seven cats,
Each cat had seven kits:
Kits, cats, sacks, and wives,
How many were there going to St. Ives?

41 A bathtub is full of water. If you have a teaspoon, a teacup, and a bucket, what's the easiest way to empty the bathtub?

42 I jump when I walk and sit when I stand. What am I?

43 If you don't keep me, I'll break. What am I?

44 Why isn't your nose 12 inches long?

45 When I am released to the wind, you look away and you pretend, but away your friends I will send. What am I?

46 Oliver's mom has 3 children. The first child's name is April. The second is May. What's the third child's name?

47 What is harder to catch the faster you run?

48 When I was 2, my sister was twice my age, and now I am 18. How old is my sister?

49   If your uncle's sister is not your aunt, then who is she to you?

50   What do people make that nobody can ever see?

51   It has dozens of limbs but can't walk? What is it?

52   What belongs to you but is used by many people you meet?

53   The more you take away, the bigger it gets.

54   I carry my home on my back. I am not rich, but I leave silver in my track. What am I?

55   You walk into a room with a rabbit holding a carrot, a pig eating slop, and a chimp holding a banana. Which animal in the room is the smartest?

56 I am no sooner spoken than broken. What am I?

57 What is full of holes but still holds water?

58 What goes up, lets out a load, then goes back down?

59 A seed am I; 3 letters make my name. Take away 2 and I still sound the same.

60 Two planes take off at the same exact moment. They are flying across the Atlantic. One leaves New York and is flying to Paris at 500 miles per hour. The other leaves Paris and is flying to New York at just 450 miles per hour. Which one will be closer to Paris when they meet?

61 What thrives when you feed it but dies when you water it?

62   What will be yesterday but was tomorrow?

63   What tastes better than it smells?

64   A black dog is sleeping in the middle of a black road that has no streetlights, and there is no moon. The driver of a car coming down the road with the lights off steers around the dog. How did the driver know the dog was there?

65   I have no feet, no hands, no wings, but I climb to the sky. What am I?

66   What state has 4 eyes but can't see?

67   I can be cracked or played, told or made. What am I?

68 I know a word of letters three. Add one letter to it and none there will be. What is the word?

69 What is easy to get into but hard to get out of?

70 A big person and a small person are going fishing. The big person is not the small person's father, but the small person is the big person's son. What is the relationship between the two?

71 What has 88 keys but cannot open a single door?

72 An old-fashioned bike wheel has 21 spokes. How many spaces are between the spokes?

73 An archaeologist unearths a coin bearing an inscription dating it to "87 BC." How does he instantly know that it's a forgery?

74 What has 1 head, 1 foot, and 4 legs?

75 You are a bus driver. At the first stop, 4 people get on. At the second stop, 8 people get on. At the third stop, 2 people get off, and at the last stop, everyone gets off. What color are the bus driver's eyes?

76 I can travel the entire world while staying in the corner. What am I?

77 A man in a 4-story building jumps out of the window and is unharmed. He used no padding. How is this possible?

78 What has a face and 2 hands but no arms or legs?

79 This ancient riddle is found in *Oedipus the King*, a play written by Sophocles in the 5th century BC: What goes on 4 legs in the morning, on 2 legs at noon, and on 3 legs in the evening?

80 If you are running a race and pass the person in second, what place are you in?

81 A plane crashes on the border of the US and Canada. Where do you bury the survivors?

82 If you are reading this, I am moving left to right. What am I?

83 You throw me out when you use me and take me in when you are done. What am I?

84   Take off my skin. I won't cry, but you will. What am I?

85   There's a land where there are mommies and daddies but no babies. Books but no libraries. Mirrors but no reflections. Kittens but no cats. Cattle but no cows. Lollipops but no candy, and trees but no forests. It's the land of what?

86   What do Alexander the Great and Winnie the Pooh have in common?

87   There is a time when they're green, a time when they're brown, and both of these times cause me to frown. But just in between, for a very short while, they're perfect and yellow and cause me to smile! What am I talking about here?

88 If you toss a regular coin 10 times and it lands on heads every time, what are the chances it will land on heads if you toss it again?

89 I am a word. If you pronounce me right, it will be wrong. If you pronounce me wrong, it is right. What word am I?

90 A woman with no driver's license goes the wrong way on a one-way street and turns left at a corner with a "No Left Turn" sign. A policeman sees her but does nothing. Why?

91 What body part is pronounced as 1 letter but written with 3, and only 2 different letters are used?

92 What is it that after you take away the whole, some still remains?

93   Two brothers were born on the same day, in the same year, and to the same mother and father, but they're not twins. How can this be?

94   I have 2 arms but fingers none. I have 2 feet but cannot run. I carry well but carry best on my wheel with my feet off the ground. What am I?

95   Jack is standing behind Jill, but Jill is standing behind Jack. How can this be possible?

96   I am easy to lift but hard to throw. What am I?

97   A mother and father have 4 daughters, and each daughter has 2 brothers. How many people are in the family?

98   A skin have I, more eyes than one. I'm good to eat when I am done. What am I?

99 A father's child, a mother's child, yet no one's son. Who am I?

100 What has 13 hearts but no other organs?

101 I am constantly overlooked by everyone, but everyone has me. What am I?

102 The rungs of a 10-foot ladder attached to the outside of a floating ship are 1 foot apart. If the water is rising at the rate of 1 foot an hour, how long will it take until the water covers the ladder?

103 What can you put in a wooden box that will make it lighter?

104 Two fathers and their 2 sons go fishing together. They each catch 1 fish to take home with them. They do not lose any

fish, and yet when they arrive home they only have 3 fish. How can this be?

105 A woman has twins who are born in 2 different years and 2 different months. How did she do it?

106 Leo Loxford, a magician, claimed to be able to throw a ping-pong ball so that it would go a short distance, come to a stop, and then reverse itself. He also added that he would not bounce the ball off any object or tie anything to it. How could he perform this trick?

107 What appears when you sit and disappears when you stand?

108 What can you share freely and still have for yourself?

109 I can sizzle like bacon, I am made with an egg. I have plenty of backbone but lack a good leg. I peel layers like onions but still remain whole. I can be long like a flagpole yet fit in a hole. What am I?

110 Almost everyone sees through me without noticing me as what lies beyond is what they seek. What am I?

111 What rock group has 4 men who don't sing?

112 Without looking at a calendar, name a boy's name using 5 consecutive first letters of 5 consecutive months.

113 It's always above the negatives yet lower than the first prime; no matter how you multiply it's the same every time.

114 How can you buy 4 suits for less than $10?

115 What question can someone ask all day long, always get completely different answers, and yet all the answers are correct?

116 My life can be measured in hours; I serve by being devoured. Thin, I am quick. Fat, I am slow. Wind is my foe.

117 Use the numbers 2, 3, 4, and 5 and the symbols + and = to make a true equation.

118 I have a little house in which I live all alone. This house has no doors or windows, and if I want to go out, I must break through the wall. What am I?

119 What loses its head in the morning but gets it back at night?

120 Three men can chop down 3 trees in 3 hours. At this rate, how many men will it take to chop down 6 trees in 6 hours?

121 I am a word of letters three; add two and fewer there will be. What am I?

122 I have roads but no pavement, rivers but no water, and cities but no buildings. What am I?

123 My voice is tender, my waist is slender, and I'm often invited to play. Yet wherever I go, I must take my bow, or else I have nothing to say. What am I?

124 A girl is sitting in a house at night that has no lights on. It's completely dark! Yet she is reading a book printed on paper. How could this be possible?

125 You have a glass of water that looks about half-full. How can you tell, using only the glass of water and no measuring device, if the glass is really half-full?

126 What runs around the whole yard without moving?

127 What is next in this sequence: JFMAMJJASON?

128 A man calls his dog from the opposite side of the river. The dog crosses the river without getting wet and without using a bridge or boat. How?

129 If you count 20 houses on your right going to the store and 20 houses on your left coming home, how many different houses did you count?

130 Open me, and you can't see me without a mirror. Close me, and you can't see me at all. What am I?

131 Three doctors said that Bill was their brother. Bill said he has no brothers. How many brothers does Bill actually have?

132 Look at me one way and I weigh a whole lot; turn me around and you'll see that I am NOT. What am I?

133 What ring is square?

134 You must choose to enter one of 3 rooms. The first is full of raging fires, the second is full of assassins with loaded guns, and the third is full of lions that haven't eaten in 3 years. Which room is safest?

135 I build bridges of silver and crowns of gold. Who am I?

136 If you drop me I'm sure to crack, but give me a smile and I'll always smile back.

137 A woman and her daughter walked into a restaurant. A man walked past and they both said, "Hello, Father." How is this possible?

138 A town has only 2 barbers. One of the barbers has a nice, tidy haircut, and the other has a shaggy, messy haircut. Which barber should you go to?

139 A chain is nailed to the wall. The chain is 10 feet long, and the center of the chain dips 5 feet from where each side of the chain is nailed to the wall. How far are the 2 ends of the chain from each other?

140 What 3 positive numbers give the same result when added *or* multiplied together?

141 What has a bottom at the top?

142 How do you make the number seven become even without addition, subtraction, multiplication, or division?

143 What came first, the chicken or the egg?

144 I am always in front and never behind. What am I?

145 Ten candles are burning in a dining room. A strong breeze blows in through an open window and extinguishes 3 of them. Assuming the wind doesn't extinguish any more candles, how many candles do you have left the next day?

146 If it has a 1-quart capacity, how many pennies can you put one at a time into an empty piggy bank?

147 You have 14 brown socks, 14 blue socks, and 14 black socks in your sock drawer. How many socks must you remove (without looking) to guarantee that you have a matched pair?

148 I have 6 eggs. I broke 2, cooked 2, and ate 2. How many eggs do I have left?

149 What starts with P and ends with E and has thousands of letters?

150 I have keys but no doors. I have space but no rooms. I allow you to enter but not leave. What am I?

151 I go in dry and come out wet; the longer I'm in, the stronger it gets. What am I?

152 I like to twirl my body but keep my head up high. After I go in, everything becomes tight. What am I?

153 What do you bury when it's alive and dig up when it's dead?

154 When can you add 2 to 11 and get 1 as the correct answer?

155 I am always on my way but never arrive today. What am I?

156 Enter through one, exit through three. Once you succeed, I am on thee. What am I?

157 I am long when I'm young and grow short as I get old. What am I?

158 I have an eye but am blind, a sea but no water, a bee but no honey, tea but no coffee, and a why but no answer. What am I?

159 The more of this there is, the less you see. What is it?

160 A bus with no passengers pulls up to a stop and 10 people get on. At the next stop, 5 people get off, and twice as many people get on as at the first stop. At the third stop, 25 get off. How many people are on the bus at this point?

161 Your mother's brother's only brother-in-law is asleep on your couch. Who is asleep on your couch?

162 Diamonds and stress have this to thank for their existence.

163 A man is working on his house and goes to the store to buy something. What he's buying costs $1 each. He buys 3742 and pays the clerk $4. What did he buy?

164 What makes you young?

165 If Jack's father is Joe's son, who is Jack to Joe?

166 Always in you, sometimes on you; if I completely surround you, I can kill you. What am I?

167 I have memories but none of my own. Whatever's on my inside is what is shown. If I'm ever different, it's because you changed me. I feel like a decoration, here for you to arrange me. What am I?

168 A girl was 10 on her last birthday and will be 12 on her next birthday. How is this possible?

169 If a doctor gives you 3 pills, telling you to take one every half-hour, how many minutes will pass between taking the first pill and the last pill?

170 What comes once in a minute, twice in a moment, but never in a thousand years?

171 There are 10 people in a house and everyone will shake hands only with people shorter than themselves. They are all different heights. How many handshakes can be made?

172 Can a man legally marry his widow's sister in the state of California?

173 How many seconds are in a year?

174 What has 3 feet but can't walk?

175 Where on Earth do the winds always blow from the south?

176 What question can you never answer yes to?

177 With pointed fangs I sit and wait; with piercing force I crunch out fate, grabbing victims, proclaiming might; physically joining with a single bite. What am I?

178 I shave every day, but my beard stays the same. What am I?

179 I am a fast vehicle spelled with the same letters forward and backward. What am I?

180 A doctor and a bus driver are both in love with the same person, an attractive woman named Diane. The bus driver had to go on a long bus trip that would last a week. Before he left, he gave Diane 7 apples. Why?

181 I'm not an airplane, but I can fly through the sky. I'm not a river, but I'm full of water. What am I?

182 If the day before yesterday was the 23rd, then what is the day after tomorrow?

183 In a lake is a patch of lily pads. Every day, the patch doubles in size. If it takes 48 days for the patch to cover the entire lake, how long would it take for the patch to cover half of the lake?

184 I can be part of your routine and hard to break. If you remove the first letter, A BIT remains. If you remove the second, BIT still remains. If you remove the third, IT still remains. What am I?

185 I have a tongue but cannot talk. I have a soul but am not alive. What am I?

186 A poor man is sitting in a pub. He sees that the man next to him is extremely rich. Poor man: "I have an amazing talent; I know almost every song that has ever existed." The rich man laughs. Poor man: "I am willing to bet you all the money you have in your wallet that I can sing a popular song that includes a lady's name of your choosing." The rich man laughs again. Rich man: "Okay, how about my daughter's

name, Sarah Catherine Williams?" The poor man goes home rich. What song did he sing?

187 I never ask questions, but I am always answered. What am I?

188 What stays the same size no matter how much they weigh?

189 What symbol can be put between 2 and 3 to make the result greater than 2 but less than 3?

190 What can run but never walks, has a mouth but never talks, has a bed but never sleeps, has a head but never weeps?

191 There are 20 people in an empty, square room. Each person has full sight of the entire room and everyone in it without turning their head or body or moving in any way.

Where can you place an apple so that all but one person can see it?

192 What goes up but never comes down?

193 What do you call the mother-in-law of your sister's husband?

194 He has married many but has never been married. Who is he?

195 A man walking along a railroad track sees a train thundering at high speed toward him. Instead of immediately jumping off the track, he charges directly at the train for about 10 feet and only then gets off the track. Why?

196 If I have it, I should not share it. If I share it, I don't have it. What is it?

197 What is bought by the yard and worn by the foot?

198 I am big on Saturday and Sunday. Small on Tuesday, Wednesday, and Thursday. I'm not on Monday or Friday. What am I?

199 A nonstop train leaves New York City for Boston at 60 mph. Another nonstop train leaves Boston for New York City at 40 mph. How far apart are the trains 1 hour before they pass each other?

200 A man is standing on a bridge and sees a boat full of people go under the bridge. He goes to the other side of the bridge but when the boat comes out, he can't see a single person. Why?

201 Max ordered a fishing rod priced at $12.34. Unfortunately, Max lives in a

remote part of Greenland and the import rules there forbid any package longer than 4 feet. The fishing rod is 5 feet long. How can the fishing rod be mailed to Max in one piece without breaking the rules?

202 A house has 4 walls. All of the walls are facing south, and a bear is circling the house. What color is the bear?

203 When I point up, it's bright, but when I point down, it's dark. What am I?

204 What letter comes next: O T T F F S S?

205 It doesn't live completely within a house, nor does it live completely without. Most will use it when they come in and again when they go out.

206 I'm not clothes, but I cover your body. The more I'm used, the thinner I get. What am I?

207 A man leaves home and turns left 3 times, only to return home facing 2 men wearing masks. Who are those two men?

208 I grow up while growing down. What am I?

209 How can you combine plus signs and five 2's to get 28?

210 I run through hills and veer around mountains. I leap over rivers and crawl through forests. Step out your door to find me. What am I?

211 When I'm first said or read, I'm quite mysterious, but when I'm explained, I'm nothing serious. What am I?

212 I can travel from there to here by disappearing and here to there by reappearing. What am I?

213 The more you take, the more you leave behind. What are they?

214 Richard bets Mark $100 that he can predict the score of the football game before it starts. Mark agrees but loses the bet. Why did Mark lose the bet?

215 In my neighborhood lives a man who weighs 200 pounds. He has 2 sons who each weigh 100 pounds. One day, they decide to cross the river on a boat to visit some friends. But the boat can carry a maximum load of only 200 pounds. How did all 3 get across the river?

216 Walk on the living, they don't even mumble. Walk on the dead, they mutter and grumble.

217 Suppose you want to cook an egg for exactly 3 minutes. You have only a 5-minute hourglass timer and a 2-minute hourglass timer. Using these 2 timers, how can you boil the egg for exactly 3 minutes?

218 I always have to work with something in my eye. What am I?

219 What was *was* before *was* was was?

220 If you eat me, my sender will eat you. What am I?

221 They have not flesh, feathers, scales, or bone. Yet they have fingers and thumbs of their own. What are they?

222 A man describes his daughters, saying, "They are all blonde but two, all brunette but two, and all redheaded but two." How many daughters does he have?

223 A man decides to buy a horse. He pays $600 for it and is very content with the strong animal. After a year, the value of the horse increased to $700, and he decides to sell the horse. But a few days later, he regrets his decision to sell the beautiful horse and buys it back. Unfortunately, he has to pay $800 to get it back, so he loses $100. After another year of owning the horse, he finally decides to sell the horse for $900. What is the overall profit the man makes?

224 What 7-letter relaxing word becomes longer when the third letter is removed?

225 If you go to the movies and you're paying, is it cheaper to take 1 friend to the movies twice or 2 friends to the movies at the same time?

226 Double my number, I'm less than a score. Half of my number is less than 4. Add 1 to my double when bakers are near. Days of the week are still greater, I fear. What number am I?

227 The day before yesterday, Meryl was 7 years old. Next year, she'll turn 10. How is this possible?

228 Three men go to a hotel. The room costs $30, so each man pays $10. Once they get to the room, the manager realizes that he overcharged them by $5, so he gives the bellboy 5 $1 bills to deliver to them. On the

way to the room, the bellboy decides that because they didn't tip him, he will pocket $2. He gets to the room and gives each of the men $1 back. Therefore, each man paid $9 ($9 x 3 = $27), and the bellboy kept $2 for a total of $29. Where is the missing dollar?

229 This riddle is solved by Bilbo Baggins in *The Hobbit*:
This thing all things devours;
Birds, beasts, trees, flowers;
Gnaws iron, bites steel;
Grinds hard stones to meal;
Slays king, ruins town,
And beats mountain down.

230 A new building containing 100 offices had just been completed. Roger was hired to paint the numbers 1 to 100 on the doors. How many times will Roger have to paint the number 9?

231 You have a barrel of oil and need to remove just 1 gallon. How do you do this if you only have a 3-gallon container and a 5-gallon container?

232 I am a protector. I sit on a bridge. One person can see right through me, while others wonder what I am hiding. What am I?

233 I have a head but no body, a heart but no blood. Just leaves and no branches, I grow without wood. What am I?

234 Six glasses are in a row. The first 3 are full of juice; the second 3 are empty. By moving only 1 glass, can you arrange them so that the empty and full glasses alternate?

235 If Mr. Miles is 90 centimeters plus half his height, how tall is he?

236 How can you divide a pizza into 8 equal slices using only 3 straight cuts?

237 Four men sat down to play. They played all night till break of day. They played for gold and not for fun with separate scores for everyone. When they came to square accounts, they all made quite fair amounts. But if none of them lost, how could all of them have gained?

238 I am a type of cheese MADE backwards. What am I?

239 I have 10 or more daughters. I have fewer than 10 daughters. I have at least 1 daughter. If only one of these statements is true, how many daughters do I have?

240 Use the 4 digits 9 9 9 9 and addition, subtraction, multiplication, and division to create an equation that equals 100.

241 Can you name 3 consecutive days without using the words Monday, Tuesday, Wednesday, Thursday, Friday, Saturday, or Sunday?

242 You have 7 tennis balls that all look identical, but 1 of them is slightly lighter than the others. Using a balance scale and only 2 separate weighings, how can you find the light tennis ball?

243 A man started to town with a fox, a goose, and a sack of corn. He came to a stream which he had to cross in a tiny boat. He could only take one across at a time. He could not leave the fox alone with the

goose or the goose alone with the corn. How did he get them all safely over the stream?

244 A bat and a ball cost $1.10. The bat costs $1 more than the ball. How much does the ball cost?

245 If 2 hours ago it was as long after 1:00 in the afternoon as it was before 1:00 in the morning, what time would it be now?

246 A king announced that a race would decide which of his 2 sons would inherit all of his wealth. The sons were to ride their camels to a certain distant city. The son whose camel reached the city *last* would be given all of the king's wealth. The sons set out on the journey. After several days of aimless wandering, they met and agreed to seek the advice

of a wise man. After listening to the wise man's advice, the sons rode the camels as quickly as possible to the designated city. What did the wise man tell the sons? They did not agree to split the wealth, and their father's decree would be followed.

247 A man buys a rope from a woman for $3 and hands the woman a $10 bill. The woman goes into the grocery store next door to get change. She returns and gives the man $7. After the man leaves, the clerk from the store comes and says, "Hey, that was a counterfeit bill you gave me." The woman gives the clerk a good bill. How much has the woman lost?

248 At school, Brian has 3 friends: Dale, John, and Mark. Two of them play football, 2 play

tennis, and 2 play golf. The friend who doesn't play golf doesn't play tennis, and the friend who doesn't play football doesn't play golf. Mark doesn't play tennis. Which sports does each person play?

249 Andrea and Suzanne decided to play tennis against each other. They bet $1 on each game they played. Andrea won 3 games, and Suzanne won $5. How many games did they play?

250 A man says: "Brothers and sisters I have none, but that man's father is my father's son." Who is he pointing at?

251 Can you guess the next letter in the series? C Y G T N L I T

252 Given a rule where 1=3, 2=3, 3=5, 4=4, 5=4, 6=3, 7=5, 8=5, 9=4, and 10=3, what does 11= and 12=?

253 What heavy 7-letter word can you take 2 away from and be left with 8?

254 If you place 1 cake of soap on a balance scale and ¾ of a cake of soap plus a ¾-pound weight on the other, the pans balance. How much does the cake of soap weigh?

255 How can you make the following equation true by drawing only one straight line: 5 + 5 + 5 = 550?

256 Donnie and Therese both have some apples. If Donnie gives Therese an apple, they will both have the same number of apples. However, if Therese gives Donnie an apple, Donnie

will have twice as many as Therese. How many apples do Donnie and Therese each have?

257 Owen is the 50th fastest and the 50th slowest runner in his school. Assuming that no 2 runners run at the same speed, how many runners are in Owen's school?

258 In a bicycle race, the man who finished 2 places in front of the last competitor finished 1 place ahead of the man who came in 5th. How many contestants were there?

259 A man has 2 ropes of varying thicknesses. He knew that each rope burns in 60 minutes, but he wants them to measure 45 minutes. How can he do that using only these 2 ropes? He can't cut the ropes.

260 Two trains are traveling toward each other on the same track, each at 60 miles per hour. When they are exactly 120 miles apart, a fly takes off from the front of one of the trains, flying toward the other train at a constant rate of 100 miles per hour. When the fly reaches the other train, it instantly changes directions and starts flying toward the other train, still at 100 miles per hour. It keeps doing this back and forth until the trains finally collide. If you add up all the distances back and forth that the fly has traveled, how much total distance has it traveled when the trains finally collide?

261 There are 12 kids in a classroom with 6 wearing socks and 4 wearing shoes. Three kids are wearing both. How many kids have bare feet?

262 What English word has 3
consecutive double letters?

263 What animal has no wings but
will fly?

264 A frog fell into a well 12 feet
deep. He could jump 3 feet, but
every time he did, he fell back
2 feet. How many times did he
have to jump to get out of the
well?

265 There are several different
kinds, but the one you pick
doesn't do its job. What is it?

266 In a stable are men and horses.
In all, there are 22 heads and
72 feet. How many men and
how many horses are in the
stable?

267 What is the largest amount of
money in coins that you can
have without being able to
make exact change for a dollar?

268 A boy has as many sisters as brothers, but each sister has only half as many sisters as brothers. How many brothers and sisters are there in the family?

269 A word I know, 6 letters it contains; subtract just 1, and 12 remain. What word am I?

270 A car's odometer shows 72927 miles, a palindromic number (the same when the digits are reversed). What are the minimum miles you would need to travel to form another?

271 It takes 10 minutes to fry 1 steak—5 minutes on each side. Two steaks can fit on a pan. What is the shortest possible time to fry 3 steaks?

272 Tomorrow is neither Wednesday nor Thursday. Yesterday was not Friday

or Saturday. Today is not Thursday, Monday, or Sunday. What day is today?

273 I am a 3-digit number. My tens digit is 5 more than my ones digit. My hundreds digit is 8 less than my tens digit. What number am I?

274 When asked how old she was, Suzie replied, "In 2 years, I will be twice as old as I was 5 years ago." How old is she?

275 If 7 people meet each other and each shakes hands only once with each of the others, how many handshakes will there have been?

276 When my father was 31, I was 8. Now he is twice as old as me. How old am I?

277 While hiking, you encounter a choice between 2 paths. One leads to the other side of the mountain, and the other will get you lost forever. Two twins know the path that leads to the other side. You can ask them only 1 question. However, 1 of the twins lies and 1 tells the truth. You don't know which is which. What can you do?

278 How high would you have to count before you use the letter A in the spelling of a number?

279 Once upon a time, there was a beautiful princess named Carla. Carla's father, the king, wanted to be sure his daughter married an intelligent man. To test his daughter's suitors, the king hid Carla's picture in 1 of 3 boxes. The suitor had to be able to select the box with Carla's picture on 1 try and

within 20 seconds. On the gold box was the message, "Carla's picture is in this box." The silver box had the message: "Carla's picture is not in this box." On the bronze box was written: "Carla's picture is not in the gold box." The king would tell each suitor, "Only one of the three messages is correct." Which box contained Carla's picture?

280   Farmer Green came to town with some watermelons. He sold half of them plus half a melon and found that he had 1 whole melon left. How many melons did he take to town?

281   Robert and Paul were in a 100-meter race. When Robert crossed the finish line, Paul was only at the 90-meter mark. Robert suggested they run another race. This time, Robert

would start 10 meters behind the starting line. All else being equal, will Paul win, lose, or tie in the second race?

282 With the digits 123456789, make them add up to 100. They must stay in the same order. You can use addition, subtraction, multiplication, and division.

283 This riddle is found in Jane Austen's 1815 novel, *Emma*. Each of the 2 sentences suggests a word. Put those 2 words together to get the answer.
My first displays the wealth and pomp of kings,
Lords of the earth! their luxury and ease.
Another view of man, my second brings,
Behold him there, the monarch of the seas!

284 Mrs. Wilhelm is a 5th-grade teacher. One of her students took her apple. Mrs. Wilhelm has narrowed the suspects down to Daniel, George, and Andrew. Each of these students offers these statements: Daniel says he didn't do it. George says he didn't do it. Andrew says George did it. Mrs. Wilhelm knows that only one of the kids is telling the truth. Which one is telling the truth, and who took the apple?

285 A professional fisherman caught 30 fish during a 5-day tournament. Each day, he caught 3 more fish than the day before. How many fish did the fisherman catch on the first day?

286 A hunter met 2 shepherds, One had 3 loaves, and the other had 5. All of the loaves

were the same size. The 3 men agreed to share the 8 loaves equally between them. After they had eaten, the hunter gave the shepherds 8 bronze coins as payment for his meal. How should the 2 shepherds fairly divide this money?

287 My age today is 3 times what it will be 3 years from now, minus 3 times what my age was 3 years ago. How old am I?

288 Find the 5-digit number in which the 1st digit is ½ of the 4th digit, the 2nd digit is ¼ of the last digit, the 4th digit is 3 times the 2nd digit, and the 3rd digit is the 1st digit plus 4.

289 You have a rope that will reach around the earth. If you put 1-meter-high sticks around the

world and lay the rope on these sticks, how much longer will the rope need to be?

290　There are 3 black hats and 2 white hats in a box. Three men (we will call them Ethan, Lucas, and Caleb) each reach into the box and place a random hat on his head. They cannot see what color hat they have chosen. The men are situated in a way that Ethan can see the hats on Lucas and Caleb's heads, Lucas can only see the hat on Caleb's head, and Caleb cannot see any hats. When Ethan is asked if he knows the color of the hat he is wearing, he says no. When Lucas is asked if he knows the color of the hat he is wearing, he also says no. When Caleb is asked if he knows the color of the hat he is wearing, he says yes—and he is correct. What color is the hat that Caleb is wearing?

291 Barry said, "I wish yesterday was tomorrow so that today would be Friday." On what day of the week did Barry say this?

292 There is a mythical land where people live for hundreds of years. In this land, a girl is twice as old as her brother and half as old as her father. In 50 years, her brother will be half as old as his father. How old is the girl now?

293 A farmer lived in a small village. He had 3 sons. One day, he gave $100 to his sons and told them to go to the market. The 3 sons were told to buy 100 animals for $100. In the market were chickens, hens, and goats. The cost of

a goat was $10, the cost of a hen was $5, and the cost of a chicken was 50 cents. They are told to purchase at least 1 animal from each group and to spend the entire $100. What did the sons buy?

294 You are blindfolded, and 10 coins are placed in front of you on a table. You are allowed to touch the coins but can't tell which way up they are by feel. You are told that there are 5 coins with heads up and 5 coins with tails up, but not which ones are which. How do you make 2 piles of coins, each with the same number of heads up? You can flip the coins any number of times.

295 In a pond are some flowers with some bees hovering over them. How many flowers and bees are there if both of the

following statements are true:
If each bee lands on a flower,
1 bee doesn't get a flower. If 2
bees share each flower, 1 flower
is left out.

296 Alice is walking through the
forest of forgetfulness. She
wants to know what day of the
week it is. She stops and asks
a lion and a unicorn. The lion
lies all the time on Monday,
Tuesday, and Wednesday.
The unicorn always lies on
Thursday, Friday, and Saturday.
When Alice asks the lion
what day it is, he says, "Well,
yesterday was one of my lying
days." Alice can't figure it out
based on the lion's answer
alone, so she asks the unicorn.
The unicorn says, "Yesterday
was also one of my lying days."
What day is it?

297 A woman went into a bank to cash an insurance refund check. By mistake, the teller gave her dollars for cents and cents for dollars. She put the money in her purse but accidentally dropped a nickel on the floor. When she got home, she found that she had exactly twice the amount of the check she had cashed. She didn't have any money in her wallet before going to the bank. What was the exact amount of that check?

298 Here is the Monty Hall problem. It is loosely based on the game show *Let's Make a Deal* and named after its host, Monty Hall. This problem gained widespread attention after Marilyn vos Savant presented it in her "Ask Marilyn" column in *Parade* magazine in 1990.

Suppose you're on a game show, and you're given the choice of 3 doors: Behind one door is a car; behind the others are goats. You pick a door, say No. 1, and the host, who knows what's behind the doors, opens another door, say No. 3, which reveals a goat. He then says to you, "Do you want to pick door No. 2?" Is it to your advantage to switch your choice?

For more information, including how it fooled many people, Google "Monty Hall Problem."

299 Here is the famous "Cheryl's Birthday" problem. It was part of the Singapore and Asian Schools Math Olympiad. It went viral in 2015 and made national news around the world!

Albert and Bernard just became friends with Cheryl,

and they want to know when her birthday is. Cheryl gives them a list of 10 possible dates:
May 15, May 16, May 19
June 17, June 18
July 14, July 16
Aug 14, Aug 15, Aug 17
Cheryl then separately tells Albert the month and Bernard the day of her birthday.
Albert: "I don't know when Cheryl's birthday is, but I know that Bernard doesn't know either."
Bernard: "At first, I didn't know when Cheryl's birthday is, but I know now."
Albert: "Then I also know when Cheryl's birthday is."
So, when is Cheryl's birthday? For more information, including how to solve this problem, Google "Cheryl's Birthday."

300 This is another type of birthday problem:

How many people do you need for the odds to be in favor (at least a 50% chance) of 2 people having the same birthday? Solving this problem requires very advanced math. Of course, it is okay to guess. But note that it takes a surprisingly small number of people for there to be a better-than-even chance that at least 2 will share a birthday. In fact, this is called the "birthday paradox." For more information, including how to solve this problem, Google "Birthday Problem."

301 Legend has it that a young Albert Einstein created this riddle and that he predicted only 2% of people would be able to solve it.

There are 5 houses in a

row. Each house is painted a different color and has a person of a different nationality living in it. Each person drinks a different beverage, smokes a different type of cigar, and owns a different animal as a pet. Using these 15 clues, which person owns the pet fish?

1. The Brit lives in the red house.
2. The Swede has a pet dog.
3. The Dane drinks tea.
4. The green house is directly to the left of the white house.
5. The person in the green house drinks coffee.
6. The person who smokes Pall Mall has a pet bird.
7. The person in the yellow house smokes Dunhill cigars.
8. The person in the center house drinks milk.
9. The Norwegian lives in the first house.

10. The person who smokes Blends lives next to the person with the pet cat.

11. The person with the pet horse lives next to the one who smokes Dunhills.

12. The person who smokes BlueMasters drinks beer.

13. The German smokes Princes.

14. The Norwegian lives next to the blue house.

15. The person who smokes Blends has a neighbor who drinks water.

ANSWERS

1   An orange

2   A towel

3   A compass

4   If what he said was true, the bottle would dissolve.

5   A ruler

6   The brain

7   An umbrella

8   An egg

9   A cold

10   A flag

11   Charcoal

12   A school

13 Because you stop looking once you find it

14 You have 2 apples.

15 A window

16 A tree

17 A coin

18 A stoplight

19 80 minutes is the same as 1 hour and 20 minutes.

20 Light

21 All 12 of them

22 A coat of paint

23 A library

24 There are no stairs. It's a 1-story house.

25 Corn

26 A spider

27 T

28 Neither—they both weigh a ton.

29 A broken clock will still be right twice a day.

30 None

31 Grandpa

32 North

33 Sink

34 Water

35 A porcupine

36 Breath

37 Your sister

38 A mouse

39 Your shadow

40 Only one person was going to St. Ives.

41 Pull the plug on the bathtub.

42 A kangaroo

43 A promise

44 Because then it would be a foot.

45 A fart

46 Oliver

47 Your breath

48 20

49 Your mother

50 Noise

51 A tree

52 Your name

53 A hole

54 A snail

55 You, hopefully

56 Silence

57 A sponge

58 An elevator

59 Pea

60 They will both be the same distance from Paris when they meet.

61 Fire

62 Today

63 A tongue

64 It was daytime.

65 Smoke

66 Mississippi

67 A joke

68 The word "one." Add an "n"
     and then you have "none."

69 Trouble

70 The big person is the small
     person's mother.

71 A piano

72 21

73 The term "BC" was not used
     until centuries after the birth of
     Christ.

74 A bed

75 The color of your eyes

76 A postage stamp

77 He jumped out from the ground floor.

78 A clock

79 A human who crawls on hands and knees as a baby, walks on 2 legs in midlife, and uses a cane in old age

80 Second place

81 Nowhere because the survivors are alive

82 Your eyes

83 An anchor

84 An onion

85 The land of double letters

86 Same middle name

87 Bananas

88   50% because the previous toss does not impact the next toss

89   Wrong

90   She's walking.

91   Eye

92   The word "wholesome"

93   They are triplets.

94   A wheelbarrow

95   They are standing back-to-back.

96   A feather

97   8

98   A potato

99   Daughter

100   A deck of playing cards

101 A nose

102 It will never cover the ladder because as the water rises, so will the floating ship.

103 Holes

104 There are just 3 people: a grandfather, son, and grandson.

105 One was born on December 31, and the other was born minutes later on January 1.

106 He threw the ping-pong ball straight up in the air.

107 Your lap

108 Knowledge

109 A snake

110 A window

111 Mount Rushmore

112 JASON: July, August, September, October, November

113 Zero

114 Buy a deck of cards.

115 What time is it?

116 A candle

117 $2 + 5 = 3 + 4$

118 A chick in an egg

119 A pillow

120 3 men

121 The word "few." Add the 2 letters E and R to make "fewer."

122 A map

123 A violin

124 The girl is reading braille.

125 Tip the glass of water until the water reaches the rim of the glass. If the water lines up perfectly with the bottom rim of the glass, it is half-full.

126 A fence

127 The letter D. The sequence contains the first letter of each month.

128 The river is frozen.

129 20 houses because the houses on your right would be the same houses on your left when you're coming back.

130 Eyes

131 None. He has 3 sisters who are doctors.

132 A ton

133 A boxing ring

134 The third room. Lions that haven't eaten in 3 years are dead.

135 A dentist

136 A mirror

137 The man was a priest.

138 The one with the messy haircut because he cuts the barber's hair with the nice haircut

139 Zero inches. Both ends are together and nailed with the same nail.

140 1, 2, and 3

141 Your legs

142 Drop the S.

143 The egg. Dinosaurs laid eggs long before there were chickens.

144 The future

145 Three—because the 7 candles that stayed lit will melt down completely

146 One, because then it will not be empty

147 4

148 4 eggs are left. The 2 broken eggs were then cooked and eaten.

149 Post Office

150 A computer keyboard

151 A teabag

152 A screw

153 A plant

154 When you add 2 hours to 11:00, you get 1:00.

155 Tomorrow

156 A T-shirt

157 A pencil

158 The alphabet

159 Darkness

160 Just 1, the driver.

161 Your father

162 Pressure

163 The number of his house for his street address.

164 Adding the letters "ng."

165 Joe is his grandfather.

166 Water

167 A picture frame

168 Today is her 11th birthday.

169 60 minutes

170 The letter M

171 Zero. For any two people one
will always be taller, and the
shorter person will not shake
hands.

172 No, he's dead.

173 Only 12: January 2nd,
February 2nd, etc.

174 A yardstick

175 The North Pole

176 Are you asleep?

177 A stapler

178 A barber

179 A racecar

180 An apple a day keeps the
doctor away!

181 A cloud

182 The 27th

183 47 days

184 The word "habit"

185 A shoe

186 The happy birthday song

187 A doorbell

188 Scales

189 A decimal point

190 A river

191 Place the apple on one person's head.

192 Your age

193 Mother

194 A priest

195 The man was on a bridge.

196 A secret

197 Carpet

198 The letter S

199 100 miles

200 They are all married.

201 Insert the fishing rod into a box that measures 4 feet on all sides. The fishing rod will fit within the diagonal of the box with room to spare.

202 White. It is a polar bear at the North Pole.

203 A light switch

204 The letter E in "Eight"

205 A front door

206 A bar of soap

207 A catcher and an umpire

208 A goose. Down is the name for the feathers that geese grow.

209 $22 + 2 + 2 + 2 = 28$

210 A road

211 A riddle

212 The letter T

213 Footsteps

214 Richard said the score would be 0-0 before the game started, and he was right.

215 First, the 2 sons rowed across the river, and 1 stayed behind on the opposite shore while the other returned in the boat to pick up his father. That son then remained behind while the father crossed the river. Then the other son rowed

the boat back to pick up his
brother and the 2 brothers
rowed over together.

216 Leaves

217 Tip both timers over at the
same time. When the 2-minute
timer runs out, drop the eggs
in and cook them until the
5-minute timer runs out.

218 A sewing needle

219 Is

220 A fishhook

221 Gloves

222 Three: a blonde, a brunette,
and a redhead

223 200

224 Lounger

225 It's cheaper to take 2 friends to the movies at the same time. If you go 2 times, you're buying 4 tickets total, but if you go at the same time, you're only buying 3.

226 6

227 Today is Jan. 1st. Yesterday, December 31st, was Meryl's 8th birthday.

228 Each man paid $9 for a total of $27. The hotel has $25, and the bellboy has $2 for a total of $27. There is no missing dollar.

229 Time

230 20: 9, 19, 29, 39, 49, 59, 69, 79, 89, 90, 91, 92, 93, 94, 95, 96, 97, 98, 99 (there are two 9's in 99)

231 Fill the 3-gallon container with oil and pour it into the 5-gallon container. Then fill

the 3-gallon container again and use it to fill the 5-gallon container the rest of the way. One gallon will be left in the 3-gallon container.

232 Sunglasses

233 Lettuce

234 Pour the juice from the second glass into the fifth glass.

235 180 centimeters

236 Cut 1: Cut the pizza into 2 halves.
Cut 2: Cut the pizza into 4 quarters.
Cut 3: Pile the 4 quarters on top of each other and cut through the middle to get 8 equal slices.

237 The men were musicians.

238 Edam

239 I have no daughters.

240 (9 divided by 9) + 99

241 Yesterday, today, and tomorrow

242 Put 3 of the balls on each side. If they are even, the ball that wasn't weighed is the light one. If they aren't even, the side that is lighter has the light ball. Of these 3 balls, 1 should be put on each side. If the sides are even then the other ball is the light one. If they aren't even, the one that is lighter is the ball you're looking for.

243 He took the goose over first and came back. Then, he took the fox across and brought the goose back. Next, he took the corn over. He came back alone and took the goose.

244 The ball costs 5 cents.

245 9 p.m.

246 The wise man told the sons
to switch camels. Then each
son would be trying to get his
brother's camel to the city first,
so his camel (rode by the other
brother) would be last.

247 $7 plus the rope.

248 Dale and John play all 3 sports,
and Mark plays none.

249 They played 11 games.

250 His son

251 S. The series is the first letter of
each word in the question: **Can
You Guess The Next Letter In
The Series?**

252 11=6 and 12=6 (the number of
letters in the number's name)

253 weights

254 3 pounds

255 Draw a diagonal line on the first plus sign and turn it into a 4. The equation then becomes: 545 + 5 = 550.

256 Donnie has 7 apples and Therese has 5 apples.

257 99

258 There were 6 contestants.

259 He will burn one of the ropes at both the ends and the second rope at one end. After 30 minutes, the first one burns completely. At this point, he will light the other end of the second rope so that now it will take 15 more minutes to completely burn. The total time will be 45 minutes.

260 100 miles

261 5

262 Bookkeeper

263 A caterpillar. It has no wings, but it will fly when it becomes a butterfly.

264 On the 10th jump, he reached the top and was out before he fell back 2 feet.

265 A lock

266 14 horses and 8 men

267 $1.19 (3 quarters, 4 dimes, and 4 pennies)

268 4 brothers and 3 sisters

269 Dozens. Remove the s and "dozen" remains.

270 110 miles to get to 73037

271 15 minutes. Start with steak 1 and steak 2. After 5 minutes, take steak 1 off, start to fry steak 3, and turn over steak 2. After 10 minutes, steak 2 is ready, and steak 1 and steak 3 need to be finished on the second side. Remove steak 2 and fry the other side of steak 1 and steak 3.

272 Friday

273 194

274 12

275 21

276 23

277 Ask either twin, "What would your brother say is the path to the other side of the mountain?" Then take the other path.

278 One thousand

279 The silver box

280 3

281 Paul will lose again. In the second race, by the time Paul reaches the 90-meter mark, Robert will have caught up to him. Therefore, the final 10 meters will belong to the faster of the two. Because Robert is faster than Paul, he will take the lead in the final 10 meters and win the race.

282 $1 + 2 + 3 + 4 + 5 + 6 + 7 + (8 \times 9) = 100$

283 The first sentence signifies "court" (the wealth and pomp of kings). The second sentence signifies "ship" (the monarch of the seas). The answer put together is "courtship."

284 George is telling the truth, and Daniel took the apple.

285 He didn't catch any fish the 1st day, but he caught 3 on the 2nd day, 6 on the 3rd day, 9 on the 4th day, and 12 on the 5th day.

286 The shepherd who had 3 loaves should get 1 coin, and the shepherd who had 5 loaves should get 7 coins.

287 18

288 32768

289 The rope must be 6.28 meters longer (= 2 Pi). No matter how big a circle is, if you extend the radius by 1 meter, the circumference will always be 6.28 meters longer.

290 Ethan must not see 2 white hats on Lucas or Caleb, or he would know that his own hat

must be black (because there are only 2 white hats). So, Ethan's answer establishes that at least 1 of the hats on Lucas and Caleb is black. Therefore, Lucas knows that he and Caleb are either both wearing black or 1 is wearing black, and 1 is wearing a white hat. If he sees that Caleb is wearing a white hat, then he would know that his own hat has to be black. But Lucas instead says he doesn't know what color hat he is wearing, which means that Caleb's hat is not white and must be black. Therefore, Caleb knows he is wearing a black hat.

291 Sunday

292 50

293 1 goat, 9 hens, and 90 chickens

294 Make 2 piles with an equal number of coins. Then, flip all the coins in one of the piles.

295 4 bees and 3 flowers

296 Thursday

297 31.63

298 The contestant should switch to the other door. The switching strategy has a two-thirds probability of winning the car, while sticking with the initial choice has only a one-third probability.

299 Cheryl's birthday is July 16.

300 Only 23 people (or more) are needed to have a better than 50% change that at least 2 will share a birthday.

301 The German owns the fish.

Thanks!

We hope you enjoyed this book.

Visit us at funster.com to discover more books that will exercise your brain while you have fun. It's a relaxing way to spend some quality time!

If you have a moment...

Amazon.com reviews are extremely important and <u>really</u> help us. Could you leave one now? This link will take you to the Amazon.com review page for this book:

<u>funster.com/review35</u>

Browse all Funster books here:
funster.com/books

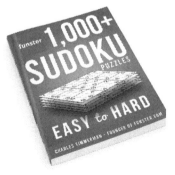

Browse all Funster books here:
funster.com/books

Made in the USA
Columbia, SC
13 April 2024

34337792R00061